Usborne Farmyard Tales
Sticker Stories

Scarecrow's Secret

Heather Amery

Illustrated by Stephen Cartwright

Language consultant: Betty Root
Series editor: Jenny Tyler

How to use this book

This book tells a story about the Boot family who live on Apple Tree Farm.
Some words in the story have been replaced by pictures.
Find the stickers that match these pictures and stick them over the top.
Each sticker has the word with it to help you read the story.

Some of the big pictures have pieces missing.
Find the stickers with the missing pieces to finish the pictures.

A yellow duck is hidden in every picture. When you have found
the duck you can put a sticker on the page.

This is Apple Tree Farm.

Mrs. Boot, the farmer, has two

children

called Poppy and Sam. She also has a

called Rusty.

dog

Mr. Boot is working in the barn.

He has cut up some poles with a .

saw

Now he is tying straw on a pole with some .

string

"What are you making, Dad?" asks Sam.

"You'll soon see," says Mr. Boot.

"Go and get my old, blue  and

 from the shed, please."

Off go Poppy and Sam.

4

Poppy and Sam bring the coat and hat.

They bring a  as well.

"It's going to be a scarecrow," says Poppy. She

stands on a ⬚ to help dress him.

"He looks like a nice old man," says Sam.

Sam finds some old  for the scarecrow.

"What shall we call him?" asks Sam.

"Let's call him Mr. Straw," says  .

"He's finished now," says Sam.

"Help me carry him, please, Poppy," says Mr. Boot.

"You bring the 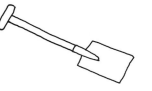 Sam."

Rusty and the 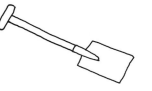 watch them.

7

They all go to the cornfield.

Mr. Boot digs a hole in the field. Then he puts the

pole in the hole so that  stands

up.  digs a hole too.

8

coat

I found the duck!

birds

I found the duck!

spade

I found the duck!

cat

kittens

I found the duck!

I found the duck!

Rusty

Poppy

I found the duck!

hat

I found the duck!

Poppy

I found the duck!

cat

box

I found the duck!

scarf

I found the duck!

rabbit

I found the duck!

birds

Mr. Straw

I found the duck!

coat

spade

I found the duck!

Rusty

I found the duck!

fence

Sam

mouse

cat

I found the duck!

Sam

"He does look real," says Poppy.

"I'm sure he will scare off all the ."

Mr. Boot rests on his 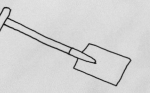 .

He looks very pleased.

The next day, they go to see Mr. Straw.

"There are no birds in the field," says  .

"Mr. Straw is doing a good job."

Rusty meets a little   .

10

They go to see Farmer Dray's scarecrow.

"He's no good," says Sam. "Those big, black  are eating all the corn."

Rusty meets a .

"Why are the birds scared of Mr. Straw?"

"I think his  is going up and down!"

shouts  . "I wonder if he's alive,"

says Sam.

"Let's go and look," says Poppy.

"We'll creep up quietly." They climb over the

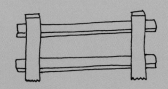 . Then they tiptoe across the

cornfield to look at  .

"There's something in his coat," says Poppy.

 sniffs at Mr. Straw.

"It's moving," says . "And it's

making a funny noise. What is it?"

Carefully they open the coat.

"It's our 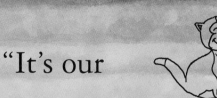," says Poppy. There is

the cat and two new baby  .

They are hiding in Mr. Straw.

15

So the scarecrow had a secret.

The was helping him frighten the birds.

"Clever cat," say Poppy and Sam.

Cover design by Vici Leyhane   Digital manipulation by Nelupa Hussain

This edition first published in 2004 by Usborne Publishing Ltd, Usborne House, 83-85 Saffron Hill, London EC1N 8RT, England. www.usborne.com